The Wind in the Willows

Based on the Novel by Kenneth Grahame
Adapted by Nomi Waldman

SCHOLASTIC INC.

New York   Toronto   London   Auckland   Sydney
Mexico City   New Delhi   Hong Kong   Buenos Aires

Illustrations
Tim Raglin

Text copyright © 2003 by Scholastic Inc.
Illustrations copyright © 2003 by Tim Raglin.
All rights reserved. Published by Scholastic Inc.
Printed in the U.S.A.

ISBN 0-439-59772-2

3   4   5   6   7   8   9   10   23   12 11 10 09 08 07 06

Contents

Welcome to This Book

What do you love more than anything? Video games? Basketball? Clothes? It's great to have something you love. But what if it gets in the way of doing other things, like your homework and chores. That's trouble, right?

Well, Toad is in trouble. Here's why. He loves sports cars. He can't resist them! He can't keep away from them. Sadly, he can't drive them either. He keeps crashing. His friends are worried. And they should be. Toad is out of control.

Can his friends help him before it's too late?

Target Words

These words will help you understand Toad's troubles.

- **adventure:** an exciting time
  Toad loves adventure.
- **escape:** to break free
  Toad had one close escape after another.
- **rescue:** to save someone in danger
  Toad's friends had to rescue him from trouble.

Reader Tips

Here's how to get the most out of this book.

- **Meet the Characters** Check out the characters on pages 6-7. Connect their names with their pictures as you read.
- **Analyze the Plot** Toad has many different adventures. Think about the different things that happen in this story. As you read, think about what happens first, what happens next, and what happens last. As you read each chapter, jot down what the main event is and who was involved. Tracking the plot will help you better understand the story.

Meet the Characters

This story takes place about 100 years ago. The characters live in the countryside of England. It seems like a place where nothing much happens. But is it?

Toad

A spoiled brat. He never listens to anyone. Will he ever learn his lesson?

Mole

A shy but curious creature. He asks his friend Rat to take him to see Badger. When Rat refuses, Mole sets out on his own adventure. But soon he's sorry.

Rat
A cheerful fellow and a good friend to everyone—even Toad.

Badger
A wise old gentleman. Everyone knows how wise he is, but few have seen him. He lives in the Wild Wood.

Weasels and Ferrets
Mean little animals. They live in the Wild Wood. You don't want to meet these guys in the dark.

1

Into the Woods

Mole sets out on his own.

Mole had always wanted to meet Badger. All the animals knew Badger was wise and important. But very few animals had met him. The one animal who knew him was Rat.

"Couldn't you invite Badger to dinner?" Mole asked his friend Rat.

"He wouldn't come," said Rat. "He hates that sort of thing."

"Then let's go visit him!" said Mole.

"He wouldn't like that," said Rat. "He's very shy. Besides, he lives in the Wild Wood. We will just have to wait for him to come to us."

And so they waited. But months went by and Badger never showed up.

So one cold, snowy day, Mole set off on his own into the Wild Wood.

Mole walks through the Wild Wood.

At first there was nothing wild at all about the Wood. Then the faces appeared.

One face peeked over Mole's shoulder. It looked mean. Then it disappeared. Then another face, meaner than the first, popped up from a hole in the ground. Then another, and another.

Next, Mole heard some whistling.

The footsteps behind Mole grew louder and louder. It seemed to him as if the whole wood was following him. In a panic, he began to run. He ran into things. He ran over things. The footsteps thundered in his head. Mole **collapsed.** He lay panting and trembling on the floor of the Wild Wood.

After a while, Mole crawled into a small cave where he huddled in fear for hours. Suddenly, he heard a friendly voice.

"Moly, Moly! Where are you?" called Rat.

"Oh Ratty!" Mole called. "Is it really you?"

Heads Up!

Look up collapse *in the glossary. What made Mole collapse?*

Rat followed the sound of his friend's voice.

"Here you are! I tried to warn you about the Wild Wood." said Rat. "Come on, I'll take you to Badger's house."

Moments later, they arrived at Badger's door.

"Who is it? Who bothers me in the middle of the night?" growled a voice behind the door.

The door swung open. Mole shook at the sight of the huge angry Badger.

"Why Ratty, my dear little man," said Badger. "What are you small animals doing out on this cold night? Come in, come in."

Badger showed Mole and Rat to a fire where they warmed themselves. They chatted about all kinds of things. Then Badger asked about their friend Toad.

"Oh, he's gone from bad to worse," said Rat. "He's crazy about cars. He keeps buying them and smashing them up. He has had seven cars and been in the hospital three times."

"This has gotten out of hand," said Badger. "This summer we will have to do something about it. We will **rescue** Toad from himself!"

2

Mr. Toad's Adventures

Can Toad's friends stop him?

Badger kept his word. It was early summer when he arrived at Rat's House. The sun was hot, and everything was green again.

Badger's first words were, "The time has finally come."

He meant it was time to help Toad.

"He has another new motor car," said Badger. "This one is even bigger than the others."

"We'll save him. He'll thank us before we're through with him," said Rat.

They picked up Mole and then Badger led the way to Toad Hall. And there was Toad. He was standing by a bright red car.

"Well, hello," Toad cried. "You're just in time. I'm about to go for a ride. And you can come with me."

Toad stands near his new motor car.

Then Toad saw the looks on his friends' faces. "Oh," was all he could say.

"Let's go inside," Badger said. Toad and the others did as Badger ordered.

Inside, Badger told Toad to come with him. "You need to hear the truth about yourself." Off they went to another room. Badger shut the door behind them.

"That won't do," said Rat. "Talking to Toad won't help."

"Why not?" asked Mole.

"He'll say anything you want him to say. But he won't mean it," answered Rat. Rat understood people.

But this time maybe he was wrong. After all, Badger was very wise.

Almost an hour passed before the two came out. Toad looked very sad. He had been crying.

Heads Up!

What do you think Badger says to Toad when they go into the other room?

"Sit down, Toad," Badger said in a kind voice. Then he turned to the other two. "I'm happy to tell you that Toad is sorry. He has promised to give up cars forever."

"That is very good news," said Mole.

"Yes, it is good news," said Rat. "But only if he means it."

Rat looked hard at Toad. He was sure he saw Toad wink one eye.

"Now, Toad," said Badger. "Repeat what you told me. Say how sorry you are about everything you've done."

There was a long, long wait. Then at last Toad spoke.

"No, I'm not sorry. It was wonderful!"

"What?" cried Badger. "Didn't you just tell me that you were sorry?"

"Oh, in there I did. I'd have said anything in there. But now I see that it's really not true. So I can't promise that again."

"You don't promise to give up cars?"

"Not at all," said Toad. "I'm leaving in the first car I see."

"I told you so," Rat said to Mole.

Mole sighed. This was one time that he wished Rat had been wrong.

"Very well then," said Badger sadly. "We will have to take care of things ourselves. We are moving in with you Toad. And we won't leave until you change!"

Heads Up!

Do you think the animals should mind their own business and leave Toad alone? Why or why not?

3

Changing Mr. Toad

Can Toad really change his ways?

"We will lock him in his bedroom," Badger announced to the others.

They dragged Toad upstairs. He fought them all the way.

"It's for your own good, you know," Rat said.

Rat pushed Toad into his bedroom. Mole locked the door.

They went downstairs again. But they could still hear Toad shouting at them.

"This may take a long time," said Badger. "We can never leave him alone. Someone must be with him at all times."

So the animals took turns staying in Toad's room. The days went on. But still, Toad would not promise to change.

Then, one morning Rat went up to take his turn. Badger told him how quiet Toad had been.

"You be careful, Rat. It's not good when Toad is quiet. It means he's planning something," Badger said. Then he walked out.

"How are you today, old friend?" asked Rat. Toad just lay quietly on his bed.

At last he answered in a weak voice. "It's so good of you to ask, dear Ratty."

"Now, do get up. Don't just lie there like that," Rat said.

"Oh, dear Ratty, I cannot get up. I'm very sick . . . but don't worry. Soon, I'll be no trouble to you at all."

Then Toad asked for a doctor.

"Why do you want a doctor?" asked Rat. It was true that Toad seemed very weak.

"Oh," said Toad, "never mind. Forget that I asked. Tomorrow it won't matter anyway."

That was too much for Rat. "Of course, I'll get the doctor for you." He went out, carefully locking the door behind him.

As soon as Rat was gone, Toad jumped up. He got dressed quickly. Then he tied all the sheets from his bed together. Down he slid from the window to the ground.

He marched off feeling very good about himself. "Oh, how good to be free," he thought. "What a clever, clever toad I am."

The happy Toad walked many miles. At last he reached a little town. By then he was hungry and tired. But right ahead of him was an **inn**, The Red Lion. He went right in and ordered a large lunch.

He was still eating when he heard a lovely sound. It was a car, a big one. He rushed outside. Two men were getting out of the car. They went into the inn. Toad walked around the motor car, looking it over.

"I wonder how it drives," he asked himself. He got in. And soon he was roaring down the road. He sang as he drove mile after mile. He drove and he sang . . . and he smashed the car.

Oh, how quickly everything changed for Toad! He went before a judge. When the judge heard what Toad had done, he became very angry. He ordered that Toad be put in a dark, dark **dungeon**—for many years.

"Is this the end?" Toad moaned. "Is this the end of poor, poor Toad?"

Weeks went by. Toad hardly ate, and nothing could cheer him up.

But Toad was lucky because the **jailer** had a daughter who felt sorry for Toad. So one day she went to Toad's cell.

"Do cheer up, Toad. And try to eat some dinner," she said.

Toad was so glad that someone cared about him. Soon he was eating and drinking and talking. The girl and Toad became good friends.

Then one day the girl surprised Toad. "Toad," she said, "How would you like to be free again? I think I know a way."

And then she told Toad how he could **escape.**

─Heads Up!─

What has happened to Toad now? How is this different from before?

20

4

More Adventures

Will Toad escape?

The jailer's daughter had a plan. She wanted Toad to change places with her aunt. Her aunt had a laundry business.

"She does the washing for all the prisoners. She picked up the clothes on Monday. So that means she'll be bringing them back on Friday. That's tomorrow. She'll give you one of her dresses. You two are about the same size."

Toad did not like the plan. "Now, really," said Toad. "You want Mr. Toad of Toad Hall to dress like an old woman?"

"Well, no, of course not," the girl said. "Just stay here for the next 20 years!"

Toad quickly said he was sorry. He promised to pay the aunt for her help.

The plan worked well. Toad and the girl tied

Toad escapes jail dressed as a laundry woman.

her aunt up. That made the escape look real. Now no one could blame her aunt.

Then Toad changed into the aunt's dress. He really did look very much like her. No one stopped him as he walked out. Soon he was a free toad.

Now he had to get back to Toad Hall. In the town, he spotted a railroad station. "Just what I need," thought Toad.

He went to buy a ticket. But something was wrong. "Oh, no!" he said. "I have no money to pay for it!"

All his cash was in the jail cell. He forgot to take it when he changed clothes!

Poor Toad could only cry.

The driver of the train heard him. "What's wrong, little mother?" he asked.

Toad cried even more. "Oh, I'm a poor, old woman," said Toad. "I've lost all my money. And I can't get home to my children!"

The driver felt bad for the poor woman. "I'll take you home," he said. Toad thanked him and got on the train. The train started, and Toad was on his way.

Suddenly another train appeared on the tracks behind them! The train driver was scared. The other train seemed to be chasing him. And it was full of police officers. They were hanging out of the train windows.

"Stop, stop!" the officers yelled.

The driver looked at Toad. Toad knew he had only one chance. He fell to his knees. This time real tears rolled down his cheeks. He sobbed as he told the driver who he really was. And then he begged, "Please, please save me. I can't go back to jail!"

The driver couldn't stand to see Toad cry. So he said he would help.

"We're coming to a thick wood. I'll slow the train down. Then you can jump out."

Toad jumped at just the right time. He rolled down a hill and then picked himself up. He hid behind a tree. Soon after, he saw the second train rush by.

Now all he had to do was follow the tracks. They would bring him home. But it would be a long, long walk.

5

Mr. Toad Goes Home

But who's living in his house?

The first friend Toad saw was Rat. Rat welcomed him home. Then he listened to Toad's whole story. The way Toad told it, he was the clever one. And he was always so brave. Nothing he did was ever wrong.

After a while, Rat stopped him. "Toad," he said, "that's enough. Go change your clothes. Then I have something to tell you!" He sounded very serious.

After lunch, Rat began to talk. "Now, I don't want to upset you. You've been through a lot. But it's really been all your own **fault.** Cars have been nothing but trouble for you. Where's the fun in that?"

Toad listened. But what was he thinking?

"It was fun," that's what Toad was thinking.

Of course, he didn't say that out loud. Out loud he said, "You are so right, Rat. After this, I really will live the quiet life. Maybe now you'll walk with me up to Toad Hall."

"Walk to Toad Hall?" cried Rat. "Do you mean you don't know?"

"Know what?" said Toad.

"The Wild Wood animals are in Toad Hall! They've taken over your home," said Rat.

"Oh, no," said Toad. "How did that happen?"

"When you got into trouble again, everyone found out. The Wild Wood animals were happy. They were sure you would not be back soon. So, one dark night, they moved in. There were weasels and ferrets—all **armed.** They chased everyone out of the house. And they've been there ever since."

Poor Toad cried when he heard that.

"We can't do anything right now," said Rat. "But maybe Badger and Mole will have some good ideas."

Toad's old friends came that very night. Everyone was happy to see Toad. And he was happy to see them.

Then Badger said, "Let's look at what's going on at Toad Hall. There are weasels all around the house. They're too strong for us."

Toad began to cry again when he heard that.

"Now cheer up, Toad," said Badger. "There is another way. I have a secret to tell you. You see, there is an underground way into Toad Hall.

"How could there be? I never heard of it," said Toad.

"Your father was my old friend, Toad. He told me this secret, not you. He thought that you, well, you talk too much."

It was true. Even Toad had to say so.

"Your father wanted me to keep this secret. He thought it might help if you ever got into trouble. Well, Toad, I'd say that time has come."

Heads Up!

What has happened so far in the story?
What do you think will happen next?

6

Mr. Toad Has Changed

But is the party really over?

In the morning, they went over their plans. Badger had heard some news.

"There's going to be a big party tonight. It's the Chief Weasel's birthday. Everyone will be in the dining room. And none of the weasels will be armed."

"But the ferrets will still be armed," said Rat.

"That's right," said Badger. "But they'll be outside. We'll be inside before they know it. There's a secret door in the kitchen. We'll rush in on them."

"And we will whack them with our sticks!" cried Toad.

"We may not need them," said Badger. "When they see us, they'll run."

The four waited until it got dark. Then they

took the underground way. It was cold and wet and dark. They had only a little **lantern** for light. The other animals were used to being underground. But Toad was not. He didn't like this **adventure** at all. But there was nothing that he could do. He, Rat, and Mole did what Badger told them. They all knew that Toad was scared.

"It's not so bad, Toad," said Mole. He was a little frightened and worried, too. But he wanted Toad to feel better.

"Don't worry, Toad," said Rat.

Toad thought that the tunnel would never end. But at last they were under Toad Hall. They could hear the party.

"They're making a lot of noise," said Badger. "That's good. They won't hear us at all."

They found the door into the kitchen. Together they pushed it up. Then, one by one, they climbed out.

Heads Up!

Rat and Mole want Toad to feel better. What kind of friends have they been to Toad?

"Now, boys, follow me!" Badger shouted.

In rushed Toad and all of his friends, swinging their sticks.

Oh, what a noise filled the air then! There were frightened animals running everywhere. All of them were screaming. Some rushed to the windows. Some hid under tables. Anything to get away from those angry sticks.

Soon it was all over. Even the weasels were gone. They ran as soon as they heard screaming.

"Well, Toad," said Badger. "We've got your house back for you. Aren't you going to give us some dinner?"

The others laughed. There was still plenty of food left from the party. They sat down at the table and ate.

Toad was back in Toad Hall again. Yet things were not the same. Other animals came to visit Toad. They told him how brave he had been.

Heads Up!

Do you think Toad will now change his character? Why or why not?

This time Toad has really changed—or has he?

But he just shook his head. Then he said the same thing to everyone.

"It wasn't me. It was my friends, Badger, Mole, and Rat. I just helped."

That was not the old Toad everyone knew. The old Toad would have taken all the credit for himself.

"But has he really changed?" his friends all wondered. Toad had fooled them before.

Only Toad knew the answer to that question.

Glossary

adventure *(noun)* an exciting time (p. 29)

armed *(adjective)* having a stick, gun, or other weapon (p. 26)

collapse *(verb)* to fall down because of weakness (p. 10)

dungeon *(noun)* a dark, underground jail (p. 19)

escape *(verb)* to break free (p. 20)

fault *(noun)* a mistake you are to blame for (p. 25)

inn *(noun)* a place where people can eat and sleep (p. 19)

jailer *(noun)* the person in charge of a jail (p. 20)

lantern *(noun)* a light with a protective frame around it (p. 29)

rescue *(verb)* to save someone in danger (p. 11)